LOOSE THREADS©

By Dave Ferry

Loose Threads©

Written, Designed & Illustrated by: Dave Ferry

www.ferryland.net

Copyright 2008 Dave Ferry

Trademark: Ferryland 2008
Published by: Ferryland® Publishing 9/2009

ISBN-13: 978-0-615-32882-9
ISBN-10: 0-615-32882-2

Printed in the U.S.A.
9/2009

LOOSE THREADS ©

By Dave Ferry

Dedicated to all rule-followers who have the courage to keep on trying, one day at a time.

Copyright 2009 Dave Ferry

G ood things should happen to good people. That's the end of it!

But most people live and observe life in the slow down lane, not the passing lane.

I was always taught to be a "Rule Follower." But where does it get you? All of us "Rule-Followers" should be rewarded with an exciting life, where life is more fair and good things happen.

"Loose Threads" is a collection of observations of the world of the "Rule Follower"...day-by-day coping with the unfair things that life throws at them, ever trying to get a break on the "Highway of Life."

Dave Ferry

Ferryland®

SLOW AHEAD

Copyright 2009 Dave Ferry

For Thelma the stakes were high.

Donald thought his first date with Sandra was going well, but he searched for a sign from her that she felt the same way.

Wendell feels a heightened sense of anxiety as he discovers his next opponent's name and picture on his own racquet.

General Perkins realized too late into his slide presentation that the final leg of the maneuvers was not a map of Italy, but a photo of his personal assistant Marjorie.

As Randy lay on an Emergency Room examining table well into the sixth hour, he became less trusting of the Doctor each time she said "Ill be right back."

Meeting Sylvia for the first time, Bill thought that his chances for sex on the first date were good. He was just uneasy about what would follow.

Storms made Webster anxious. He hoped that
the electricity would come back on soon.

"This is your Captain speaking. We have experienced a sudden loss of cabin pressure. For those of you who prefer oxygen, please deposit two dollars."

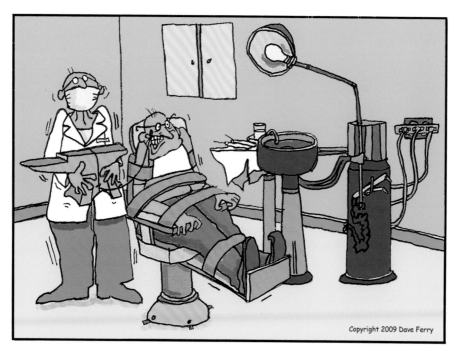

Nigel had an uneasy feeling that his new dentist wasn't keeping pace with technology.

Phillip thought that airline restrictions had gone too far.

Dr. Ramsay soon discovered what had been blocking Ralph's sinus'.

Copyright 2009 Dave Ferry

Phillip felt an attraction to Gloria but he sensed she came with a lot of baggage.

Lester stared at the jumbo fried platter...and it stared back.

Richard wished now that he had turned on the light to dress before leaving his girlfriend Phyllis' apartment.

Morty will shortly learn that he has purchased a one of a kind carved likeness of President James Polk for $17,000.

Bernice could sense that things were about to get ugly.

As Thomas learns the game of tennis, he struggles to sort out his athletic past.

As Marty completed his last session to control his anxiety, Dr. Erskine told him about a new study linking plastic bottled water to shrinking.

Thomas's earlier premonition of being 'shown the way' by an Angel soon lost it's significance.

27

Bernard didn't have to set the alarm. His
bladder had never let him down before.

"And now for my rates...Are you feeling lucky, Punk?"

Walter was inexplicably drawn to the 1930 Bentley with its topless wide body, visible spare tire, and spacious rear end.

31

Old Sparky was a very loyal dog, always at his Master's side.
Loyalty was not the issue.

All eyes turned from the T.V. as Craig received his Meds
each night at bedtime.

The airline attendant's safety talk on Phil and Larry's first
Trans Atlantic flight only heightened their uneasiness.

Raymond feels confident that he has cleverly deceived head nurse Swensen as she makes her daily check of food and liquid intake.

As Walter's last quarter slipped between the grating, his sense of relief was quickly overshadowed by a colon that felt betrayed.

Walt finishes his match profile with heightened anticipation.

Janice could sense that Willard was a "glass 3/4's empty" kind of guy.

The Ad said "In need of cosmetic work." The Anderson's were skeptical.

Andrew's relationships with women were often very brief.

Other Random Thoughts:

When asked if Maynard had any "racing thoughts" he would often pick the daily winner of the third race at Belmont.

Margaret's treatment for paranoia suddenly suffered a set-back as she was quite certain that she hadn't ordered a pineapple for dinner.

"Why can't he just dart across like the rest of us?!"

Crafts Day at the Home had been good for Nigel as he learned to hone new skills.

"And now as a special treat this evening this next item for bid includes our assistant Evelyn who apparently has an emotional attachment to it."

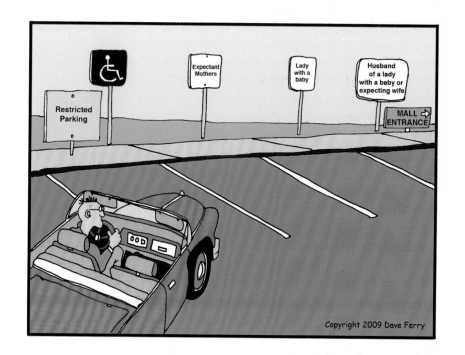

Cheating the vending machine was a game
Randolph thought he was winning.

"Children now listen up. Mr. Winkle will be the volunteer chaperone for our field trip today. He was just paroled from prison, has a nasty rash and a short temper, so I know you'll all behave."

Chester and Doreen would soon realize that they were in for a long afternoon as the Senior's Matinee crowd strained to understand the opening credits.

McFee's inner voice said "Hi Ho Silver!"
His neighbor's inner voice said "Call the Police!"